FILE UNDER BIFF

File under BIFF
Chris Garratt & Mick Kidd

A METHUEN PAPERBACK

A Methuen Paperback

First published in Great Britain in 1988
by Methuen London, Michelin House, 81 Fulham Road, London SW3 6RB
© 1986, 1987, 1988 Biff Products
Printed in Great Britain
by Redwood Burn Ltd, Trowbridge, Wiltshire

British Library Cataloguing in Publication Data

Garratt, Chris
File under Biff.
1. English humorous strip cartoons –
Collections from individual artists
I. Title   II. Kidd, Mick
741.5′942

ISBN 0–413–17660–6

BIFF PRODUCTS 1987

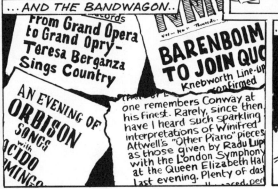

© 1987 BIFF PRODUCTS.

© 1987 BIFF PRODUCTS

FOCUS ON THEATRE

THIS WEEK: MIKE RANDALL

The props are mimed. Gesture is cut to a minimum. Mike Randall likes it that way.

The actors are paramount, yet redund--ant. That's how Mike Randall likes it.

No lights. No scenery. No script. No money. Mike Randall prefers it like that.

The stage is a deserted warehouse, the audience a transitory tide. These pose no problems for Mike Randall.

In fact, Mike Randall has nothing to do with theatre whatsoever. He runs a lawn–mower repair shop in Nottingham.

Friday ★ ★ ★ Night Fever

Tender Complete Story

THE WEEKEND.. AND I WAS FEELIN' KINDA LONESOME AN' BLUE, WHEN....

...JUST ACCEPT IT TONY...YOU WEREN'T RIGHT FOR EACH OTHER... LOOK- WHY DON'T YOU COME OUT WITH BAZ AND ME...WE'RE GOING TO THE WORKS DISCO! DUCK A L'ORANGE...PLENTY OF BOOZE...BOOGIE ALL NIGHT...

I DUNNO JENNY.... I'M SPOILT FOR CHOICE HERE...I'D LIKE TO GO TO MIKE 'N' DEBBI'S FARE-WELL BASH...AND I SAID I'D LOOK IN ON MY STUDENTS' PARTY...

LATER...

THUD THUD TITTA UP THUD

COME ON BAZ - LET'S BOP!

ENJOYING YOURSELF, TONE?

THIS IS HORRENDOUS! LET'S BLOW THIS DIVE AND TRUCK ROUND TO THE STUDENTS' PAD...SHOULD BE PLENTY OF WACCY BACCY ETC....

THESE YOUNG PEOPLE DON'T KNOW HOW TO ENJOY THEMSELVES!

I KNOW...I JUST ASKED IF THERE WAS ANY STASH...THE DUDE JUST FROZE ME OUT!

PSST! WHO ARE THE OTHER TWO WRINKLIES?

WHADDYA SAY WE SPLIT?

TAP TAP

DUNNO - I THINK THEY MIGHT BE FROM THE DRUGS SQUAD!

NEVER HAVE I FELT SO OLD! THEIR PARENTS ARE PROBABLY YOUNGER THAN US! I KNEW I SHOULD HAVE GONE TO MIKE 'N' DEBBI'S IN THE FIRST PLACE!

MIKE 'N' DEBBI'S PLACE, CABBIE... -AND STEP ON IT!

WOW! I THOUGHT THEY'D NEVER GO!

TAXI

BURNING RUBBER.

EXCELLENT PHOTOGRAPHY YOU HAVE TO ADMIT...

ACTUALLY I'M THINKING OF MOVING INTO DRAMA DOC...

I BROUGHT IT IN UNDER BUDGET... HALF A MILLION ALL IN

AH...THIS IS MORE **LIKE** IT!

I DON'T LIKE ASKING PEOPLE WHAT THEY DO... SO..WOULD YOU LIKE A DRINK?*

SACRÉ BLEU! SOMEONE **SPOKE** TO ME!

GOT ANY R&B?

..NOW TELL ME WHAT YOU'RE **REALLY** FEELING...

*NOBODY TALKS LIKE THIS. —ed.

I LOOKED AT MY WATCH IT WAS A QUARTER TO 3 AND EVERY DANCE SHE DANCED SHE DANCED WITH ME!...

YOU'RE BREAKING MY ARM, YOU LUG-HEAD!

THIS IS INCREDIBLE! YOU'RE THE FIRST PERSON I'VE MET WHO JIVES THE SAME WAY AS ME

REELIN AND ROCKIN' ROLLIN' TILL THE BREAK OF DAWN

UNTIL—IN A MAELSTROM OF SPINNING STARS..

I'D BETTER BUNG ON A SLOW ONE!

ZE FAT ONE - HE'S FALLEN OVER!

URRGH!

CRASH!

TONY'S PASSED OUT AS USUAL

I THINK I'VE SPRAINED MY NECK

-BETTER TAKE HIM HOME, I GUESS.

TURNROUND! TURN TH'BLOODY CAB ROUND! GODDAMMIT! I NEVER GOT HER PHONUMBER! (SLUR.. DROOL...MUMBLE...) DY'REELSSS SI'LL NIVERSRAGAN!...URRGH!.. I'M IN **LOVE!!**

YOU'RE AN INCURABLE ROMANTIC, TONY- YOU'RE SUPPOSED TO BE A HAPPILY DIVORCED MAN...

NEXT DAY, AT THE MENS' GROUP..

....AND I NEVER EVEN GOT HER NUMBER, KEITH... WHAT SHOULD I DO?

DON'T ASK **ME** TONY... SAME THING HAPPENED TO ME LAST WEEK..FANTASTIC CHEMISTRY...ACROSS A CROWDED ROOM...I WROTE HER NUMBER ON A FAG PACKET AND NEXT MORNING I COULDN'T EVEN READ MY OWN WRITING...MUSTA BEEN REALLY OUT OF IT...

IT'S AN ALL TOO FAMILIAR EXPERIENCE I'M AFRAID...I REMEMBER BACK IN 76...

OH NO.. NOT THE PILE-OF-COATS-ON-THE-BED STORY AGAIN!

ALL I EVER GOT ON THE MORNING AFTER WAS NUMBER UNOBTAINABLE...

I THINK THE GUY WITH HER WAS PROBABLY HER HUSBAND, ON REFLECTION...

MAKES ONE FEEL ABOUT 16 YEARS OLD!

I REALLY THINK IT HELPS TO TALK THESE FEELINGS OUT.

THIS IS WHAT WE SHRINKS CALL THE **GLASS SLIPPER SYNDROME**...A SUBCONSCIOUS FEAR OF COMMITMENT... VERY COMMON THIS TIME OF YEAR!

DAFT! I CALL IT!

MENS' GROUP
CALENDAR FOR DECEMBER

DEC 8 LEARNING TO FEEL. DISCUSSION
DEC 15 SANDAL-MAKING WORKSHOP
DEC 22 XMAS PARTY. LIVE MUSIC FUR 'N' FEATHER TOMBOLA

IMAGINARY LANDSCAPE

...of the style. Whether it's the unashamed luxury of the Montego Mayfair 1.6, the sophisticated Rover 216S, the irresistible Maestro HL 1.6, the dynamic MG Metro 1.3, the classic Mini Mayfair or the superb looking Mini City - What a prize to have ... de 946 Bayham Street

WOW!

THIS IS MY **LUCKY DAY!** MAYBE THIS IS THE MORNING I GET TO THE SHOP BEFORE THEY RUN OUT OF CROISSANTS!

YE GODS! WHAT'S **THIS?**

"YOU ARE INVITED TO APPEAR ON **DESERT ISLAND DISCS!** PLEASE BRING THIS LETTER WITH YOU TO RECEPTION....

.... **P.S.** MR. PARKINSON REMINDS ME TO ASK YOU TO SELECT **8 RECORDS** IN ADVANCE..."

Q. YOU'VE LED A LIFE OF MANY PARTS— WHICH ONE GAVE YOU MOST SATISFACTION, WOULD YOU SAY?

A. OH...THAT'S DIFFICULT.. ... I THINK I'D HAVE TO GO FOR LEAR...

Q. AND YOUR FIRST CHOICE OF RECORD?..

—BETTER COMPILE A SHORTLIST OF **TUNES!**

LET'S SEE... DVORAK? VELVET UNDERGROUND?

...MMM...MIGHT SEEM TRENDY... **DYLAN?**... ..NO...TOO CLICHED...

..**RIMSKY-KORSAKOV?**.

—BETTER PICK SOME--THING ATONAL, TO APPEAR MODERN...

---

3 DAYS LATER...

YOU LOOK GHASTLY! WHAT'S UP? CAN'T YOU REMEMBER YOUR LINES?

IT'S NOT THAT... I'M GOING CRAZY TRY--ING TO GET A DEFINITIVE **PLAYLIST**... I CAN'T DECIDE WHETHER TO GO FOR EMOTIONAL RECALL OR CEREBRAL QUALITY... ANY IDEAS?

WHY NOT LISTEN TO A FEW OTHER **CASTAWAYS?** —SEE WHAT THEY COME UP WITH?

FRIDAY MORNING...

CLICK! HI FANS—THIS WEEK'S CASTAWAY IS AVANT-GARDE COMPOSER **JOHN CAGE**.... JOHN...YOUR FATHER INVENTED A MACHINE FOR REMOVING CHEWING GUM FROM CARPETS DIDN'T HE?

THAT'S RIGHT, MIKEY...THAT'S BECAUSE HE WAS TOO MEAN TO BUY ME FRESH GUM.

WAS IT A SUCCESS—THE MACHINE?

IN A WAY, YES... I INCORPORATED IT INTO ONE OF MY EARLIER COMPOSITIONS, WHICH, I BELIEVE WAS COVERED OVER HERE BY LONNIE DONNEGAN....

DO YOU THINK WE'RE IN FOR AN ALE **TORIC** REVIVAL?

I'M NOT SO SURE... IN THESE UNCERTAIN TIMES, THE KIDS SEEM TO PREFER A STEADY 4 -TO-THE-BAR.. —ALTHOUGH I UNDERSTAND RICHARD CLAYDERMAN IS THINKING OF INCLUDING SOME OF MY NUTS'N'BOLTS PIANO PIECES IN HIS ACT....

DO YOU STILL COLLECT MUSHROOMS?

NOT SO MUCH THESE DAYS... I USUALLY PICK SOME UP AT THE GROCERY STORE, OR JUST OPEN A CAN....

Handel's Largo
Buddy Holly
Sparky's Magic Piano
Galleria Rusticana ?
Theme from 2001
Tijuana Taxi
...
Good Golly Miss Molly
Nimrod (Elgar)
Galway-Annie's Song
...

AND HOW ABOUT SOME MUSIC...WHAT HAVE YOU CHOSEN?

OH—ANY OLD STUFF....

JUST PLAY ALL EIGHT OF 'EM AT THE SAME TIME...

...MMM... —LOVELY!

FAR OUT!

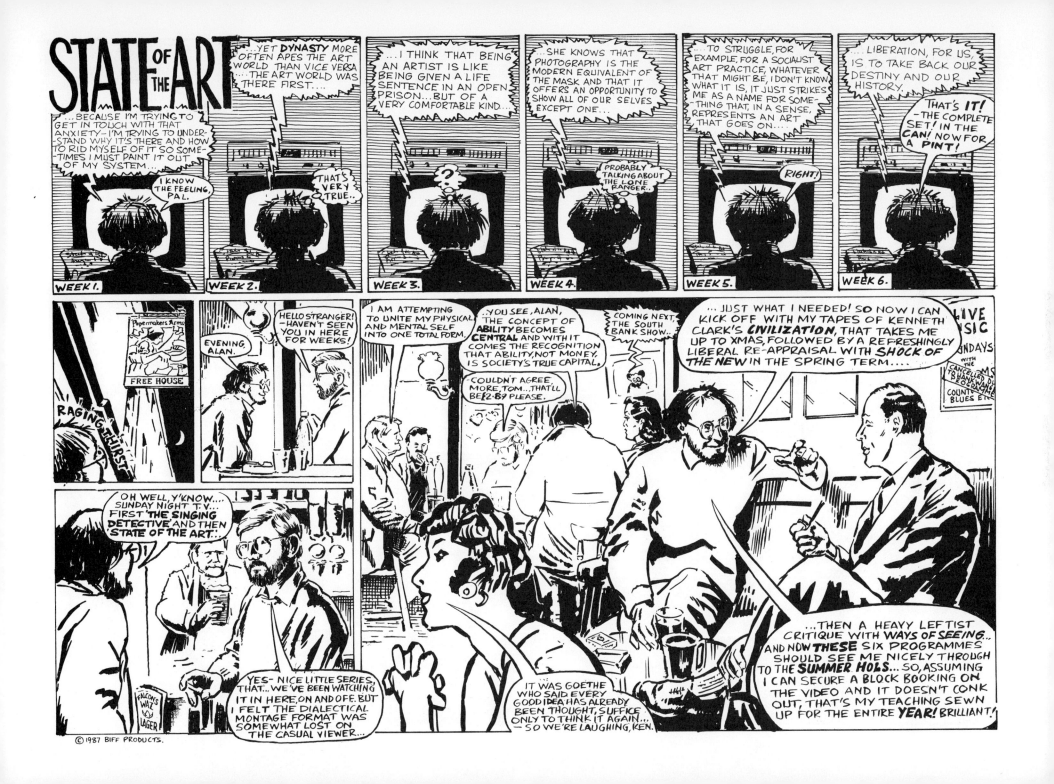

© 1987 BIFF PRODUCTS.

Dejeuner Sur L'art

© 1987 BIFF PRODUCTS.

DEALING WITH SUCCESS ★★

CITYSCAPES Nº4: YUPPY BARS ★★★★

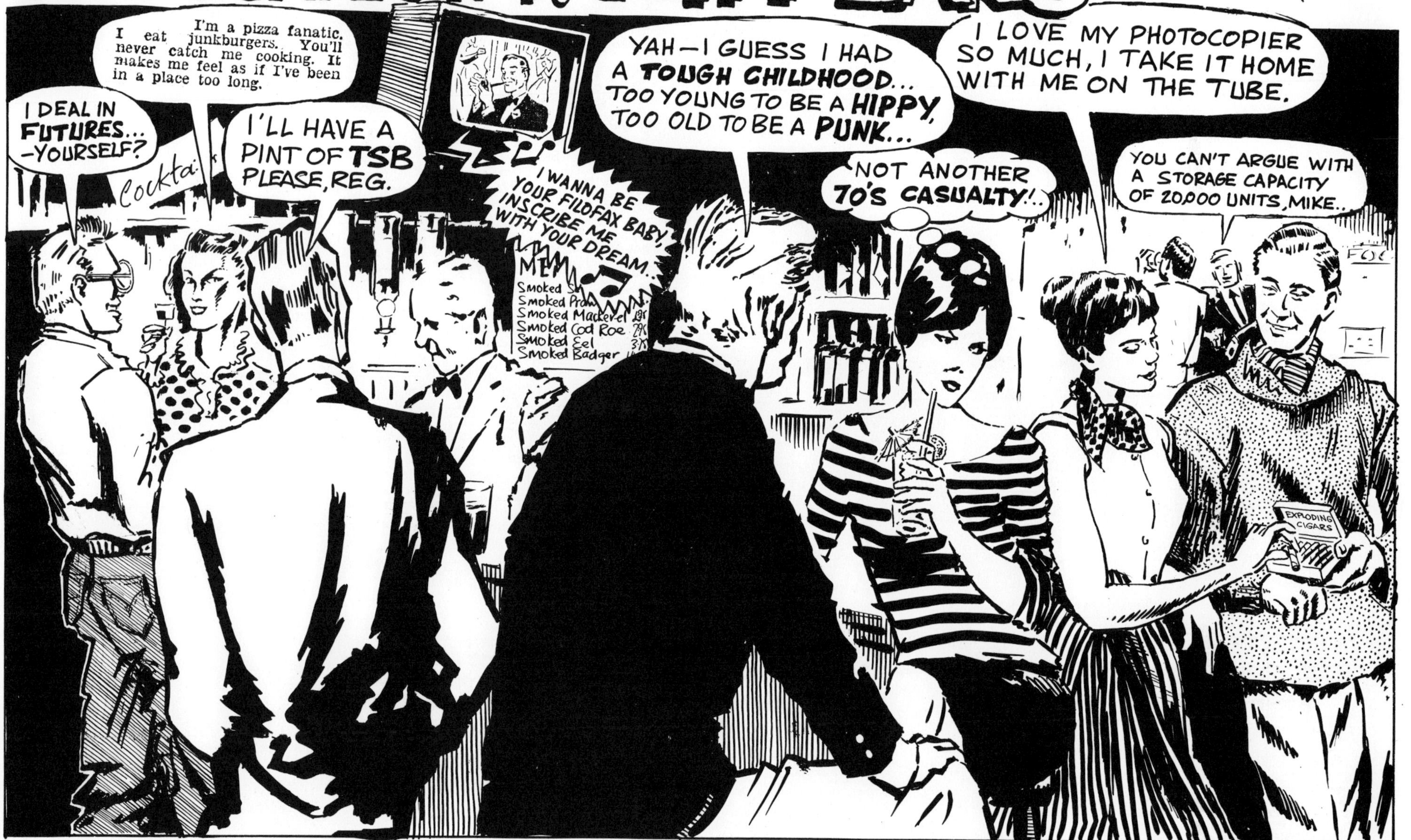

BIFF PRODUCTS

©1986 BIFF PRODUCTS

DESIGNER LIVING: ▶

AT HOME

WITH TYCOON, COLLECTOR AND WINE EXPERT GERRY BRENT

Sincerely Gerry

I MET GERRY OUTSIDE HIS HOUSE IN WILDER ST. E1, WHERE HE HAS LOVINGLY RESTORED IT TO **MID-70s** LIVING.....RIGHT DOWN TO THE CANDLES AND JOSS-STICKS...

I'VE COME TO READ THE GAS-METER, PAL.

CAN YOU COME BACK TOMORROW?....I'M EXPECTING SOME PEOPLE FROM THE QUALITY SUNDAYS.

BEEP BEEP

I THINK YOU WANT **ME**.... DO YOU LIVE IN THIS HOUSE, SIR?

....A HANDSHAKE....2 EMPTY CHAIRS WAITING TO BE FILLED...A SENSE OF ACTION THROBBED IN THE AIR, ALREADY ALIVE WITH BIRDSONG. WE SAT AT THE TABLE IN THE KITCHEN, A VIVID AND EXOTIC PLACE. "THE TABLE IS BRAZILIAN," HE TOLD ME OVER BLEND 37, "A SPLENDID PIECE IN OLD COLONIAL STYLE WITH A REMOVABLE TOP, RESTING ON TRESTLES AND MADE OF JACARANDA."

YEAH... I FOUND IT IN A SKIP...

HERE, HE HAS CREATED A ROOM FULL OF SURPRISES, WITH A MIXTURE OF OBJECTS FROM ALL PARTS OF THE WORLD, A VISUAL HUBBUB THAT ALSO WORKS AS AN EFFICIENT STUDY.....

...BUT I'M A GREAT HOARDER. ONCE YOU HAVE THE TINIEST PREFERENCE FOR THINGS, PEOPLE GIVE YOU THEM BY THE TRUCKLOAD...CAREFUL WITH THAT YOGHURT—IT'S LIVE...

PONG

FRANKIE

SUP UP AND I'LL SHOW YOU ROUND THE REST OF MY PAD

....AND **THIS ROOM** IS EMPTY. I LIKE TO HAVE CONTRAST. THIS IS WHERE I SIT AND CONTEMPLATE, WATCH TELLY OR REPLAY VIDEOS. —HOW ABOUT SOME **VINO**?

COMING NEXT—THE DIMINUTIVE SEXOLOGIST AND CHAT SHOW HOST....

......FOR GERRY, LUNCH IS USUALLY A BUN ON THE RUN, SO THE **WINE GROTTO** PROVIDES WELCOME SANCTUARY FROM THE PRESSURES OF THE DAY...

I DON'T CALL IT DRINKING... I CALL IT **ADVENTURES IN GRAPE.**

AM I RIGHT IN THINKING THIS IS A DON CORTEZ 86?

PK RIOT

OOPS!

CRASH!

NOW, IF YOU COME THROUGH HERE, —WATCH THE STEP— YOU'LL SEE I'M IN THE **SOFA GAME** NOW...

SOFA CITY BEST PRICES PAID NEW & USED SOFAS HOUSES CLEARED VINYL REPAIRS

...HOWEVER, I HAVEN'T FORGOTTEN MY ROOTS, I SHAVE AT THE BARBER'S FREQUENTLY AS A SOCIAL EVENT... DO I RECEIVE A FEE FOR THIS?

BUNG AN INVOICE IN TO US... I MUST BE OFF NOW ♪HIC♪ I HAVE TO MEET DAVID BOWIE AT 40 OUTSIDE COCO CHANEL'S ROCHETEAU APARTMENT CE SOIR....

LURCH

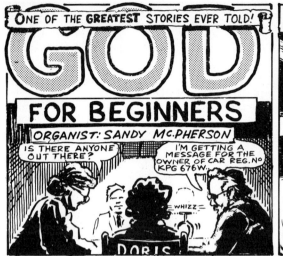

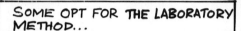

matters arising...

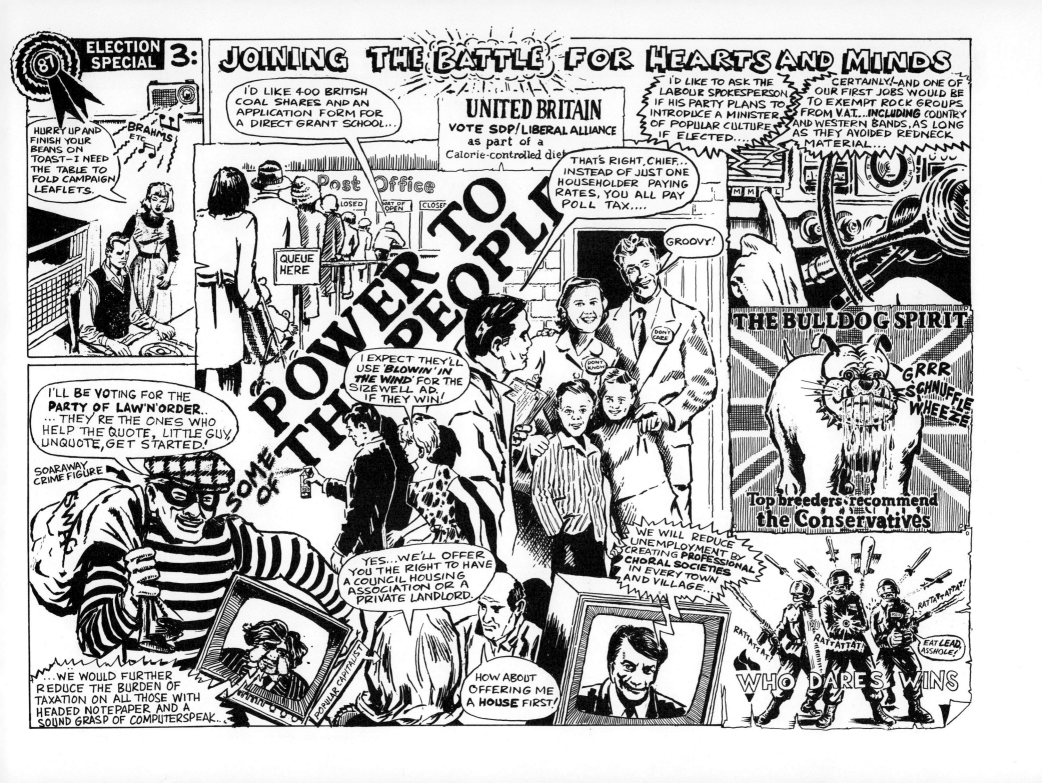

HEALTH & LIVING

BIFF PRODUCTS 1987.

© 1987 Biff Products.

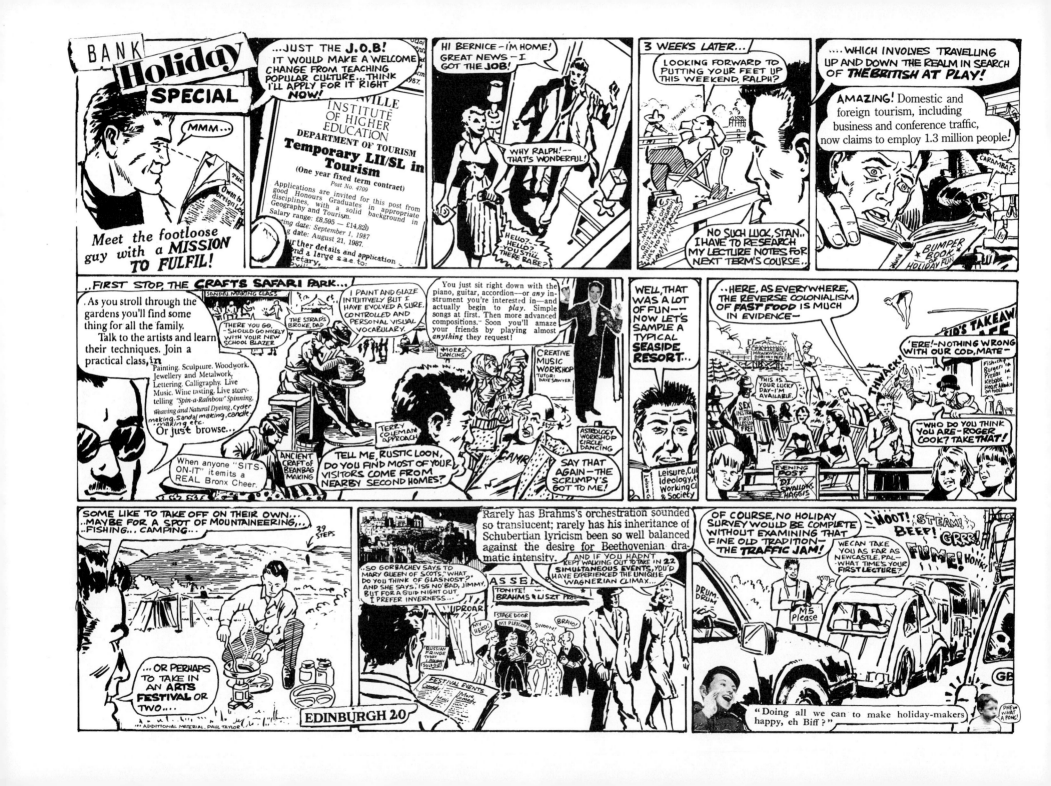

LATE NITE LINE-UP

HATS OFF TO LARRY

© BIFF PRODUCTS 1987

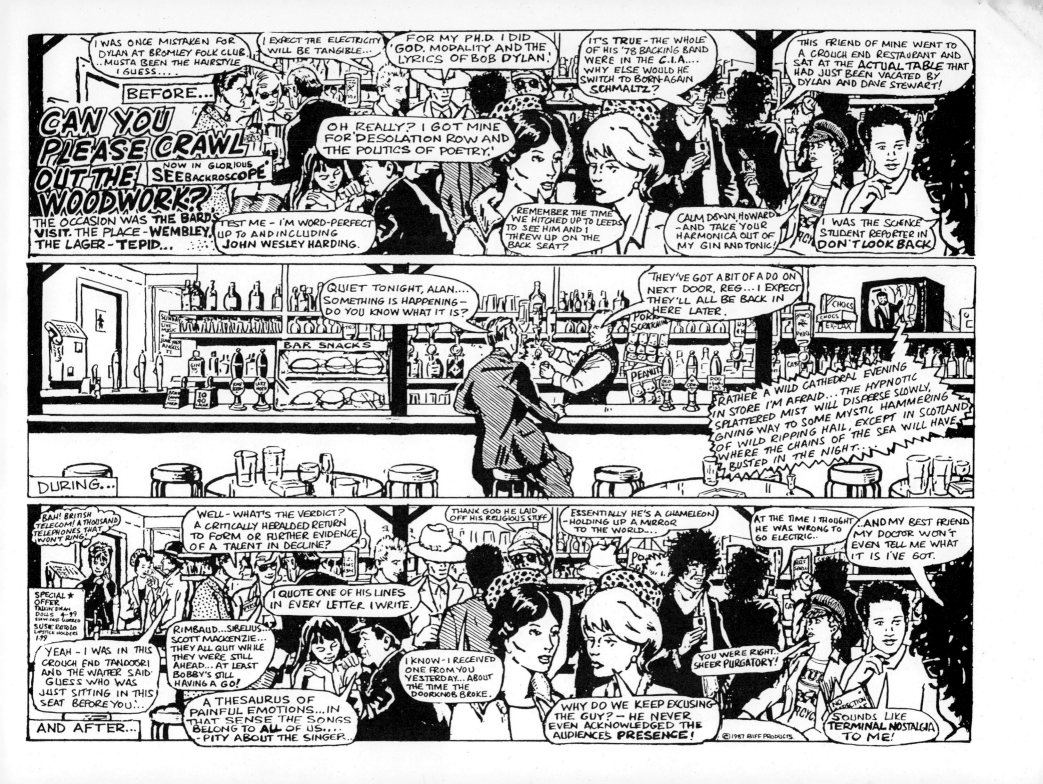

IN GLORIOUS SENSURAMA!

THE CRITIC THAT TIME FORGOT!

LONDON... NOVEMBER...
FEAR WALKS THE STREETS..

© 1986 BIFF PRODUCTS

© 1988 BIFF PRODUCTS.

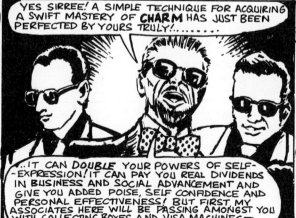

© 1986 BIFF PRODUCTS

© 1987 BIFF PRODUCTS.

CAN YOU COME BACK NEXT WEEK?

HE FLEW IN FROM **BERLIN** AND TOOK A CAB STRAIGHT TO THE **GALLERY**...

INFORMA BOX OF

HELLO — I'M HERE TO DO TONIGHT'S READING FROM MY NEW BOOK...6.30 IN THE LECTURE ROOM?

OH...YEAH...RIGHT... I'LL SEE IF **JANE'S** AROUND — SHE'S THE ONE WHO DEALS WITH TALKS...

NO SMOKING IN HERE, BY THE WAY.

THE **FACE**

HI! SORRY TO KEEP YOU WAITING.....I'M **DEE** — JANE'S AWAY ON HOLIDAY TILL FRIDAY...

...ACTUALLY, **I'M** OFF TOMORROW, — CAN'T **WAIT!**

I HAVEN'T SEEN MUCH **ADVERTISING** FOR THIS GIG....DID YOU GET MY **PRESS RELEASE?**

BAR AND RESTAUR

AH YES — WE'RE HAVING A BIT OF A FEUD WITH OUR PUBLICITY DEPARTMENT AT PRESENT, SO THEY LEAVE ALL OUR STUFF TILL LAST....WOULD YOU LIKE A DRINK?

I'LL LEAVE YOU WITH **LIZ** — SHE HANDLES ALL THE ROOM BOOKINGS... EVERYTHING O.K LIZ?

RESTAUR

GOD, I FEEL ROUGH!

WELL, JUST A **SLIGHT** PROBLEM, — THE ROOM'S NEEDED AT **7.30** FOR A LECTURE BY THIS REALLY FAMOUS FRENCH PSYCHOLOGIST, I FORGET HIS NAME....SO —

— IF YOU COULD BE OUT OF THERE BY, SAY, **7.15?**

BIFF PRODUCTS

LATER...

"...OUTSIDE, IN THE YARD BEHIND THE KITCHEN, THE CHEF URINATED INTO A BIN OF OFFAL, LAUGHING AT THE STARS."

O.K. THANKS..WELL, THAT HAS TO BE **IT,** UNFORTUNATELY. AS THEY SAY ON T.V., WE'VE RUN RIGHT OUT OF **TIME,** BUT, IF THERE **ARE** ANY QUESTIONS I'M SURE WE CAN FIND A CORNER IN THE BAR AREA... REGRETTABLY I CAN'T BE THERE MYSELF BUT...

IN THE BAR AREA

AH BONSOIR, JE SUIS M. LEGUMIÈRE, LE PHILOSOPHE CÉLÈBRE, — OÙ SE TROUVE LE GENTS?

OH, YAH...ER..DOWN LES ESCALIERS, A LA GAUCHE...ER...UN PETIT PROBLEM A CE MOMENT — NOUS AVONS UNE DELUGE...LES BUNGED-UP DRAINS...

NO SINGALONGS DISCUSSION IN PROGRESS

WOULD YOU SAY THAT YOUR DARKLY AMBIVALENT IMAGES OF THE WORKING CLASSES OWED MORE TO ORWELL OR TO LAWRENCE?

IS THERE AN INDIAN RESTAURANT ROUND HERE?

© 1988 BIFF PRODUCTS

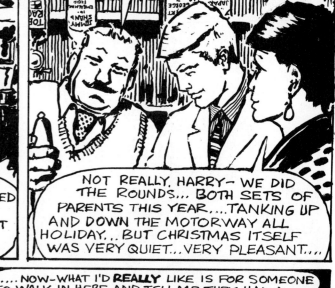

© 1987 BIFF PRODUCTS